THE
HISTORICAL HEROINES
COLORING BOOK

Pioneering Women in Science
from the 18th and 19th Centuries

Written by Elizabeth Lorayne
Illustrated by Kendra Shedenhelm
Edited by Michael D. Barton

white wave
press

Printed in the United States of America.

First printing 2017.

ISBN 978-0-9979098-7-6

White Wave Press | Newburyport, MA

WhiteWavePressBooks.com | Historical-Heroines.com

For:

Genevieve Elizabeth
Archer Nebraska
Afton Lee
Patrick Dylan

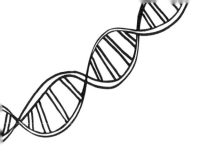

Introduction

I was incredibly fortunate throughout my upbringing in Seattle, Washington and throughout college to have attended schools with exceptional science programs. I was exposed to robotics, computer languages, biology, chemistry, paleontology, primatology, anthropology, and psychology. With this expansive curriculum and supportive, encouraging teachers, I was able to learn about science, technology, engineering, and mathematics with a honed sense of inquisitiveness, and I grew to gain confidence in my own abilities.

When I began to study the humanities, I learned about the very real discrimination women have faced, particularly in the 18th and 19th centuries. How could women possibly have been told they couldn't officially attend college, or be paid for their intellectual contributions? How could women be so unjustly treated because of their gender? In the case of many of the women, born prior to the 19th century and whose stories are told in the following pages, they were discriminated against because they were women. However, what's most remarkable is how hard these women worked to pursue their passions, their dreams, and their talents despite this discrimination. These women scientists are incredible role models — showing us that no matter the obstacles, when you persevere, you can achieve anything!

My hope is that through coloring these illustrations of strong, brilliant, hard-working women scientists, you will feel inspired to go forth and seize your own dreams and that you will in turn continue the circle of empowering yourself and others. I hope you will be encouraged to stand up against discrimination and to advocate for more and more girls to pursue fields in S.T.E.M. The women appear in order of their first names, and included in the back of the book are a glossary of terms and a resources section for further education.

This coloring book was a multi-person effort. I would like to thank artist Kendra Shedenhelm and science historian Michael D. Barton for their incredible work and contributions to this book. Above all, I want to thank our backers on Kickstarter! We live in a time that can be truly empowering and entrepreneurial. I am honored that *The Historical Heroines Coloring Book: Pioneering Women in Science from the 18th and 19th Centuries* received full support through crowdfunding. It shows just how much we need to keep finding ways to encourage not just each other, but especially ideas that have the potential to inspire children.

Elizabeth Lorayne

Ada Lovelace

1815–1852

Ada Lovelace, born in 1815 in London, England, was the daughter of renowned poet, Lord Byron. Ada's mother was interested in mathematics and preferred her daughter to follow in her predictable and reasonable footsteps rather than her father's romantic poetic tendencies.

Ada would soon prove the ingenuity of combining her innate talents for mathematics and creativity. At the young age of twelve she created plans for a flying machine and concept that she named "Flyology." And upon an introduction by her tutor, Mary Somerville, inspiration struck again when Ada met mathematician and computer pioneer Charles Babbage and learned about his machines, the **Difference Engine** and the **Analytical Machine**. She felt driven to prove her mathematical abilities to Babbage.

Through translating a French article on the Analytical Machine into English, she added detailed notes that are considered to be the first computer program, an **algorithm** the "computer" would process using punch cards. She envisioned a bigger future for the general purpose computer, outside of calculating, and imagined how it could change society.

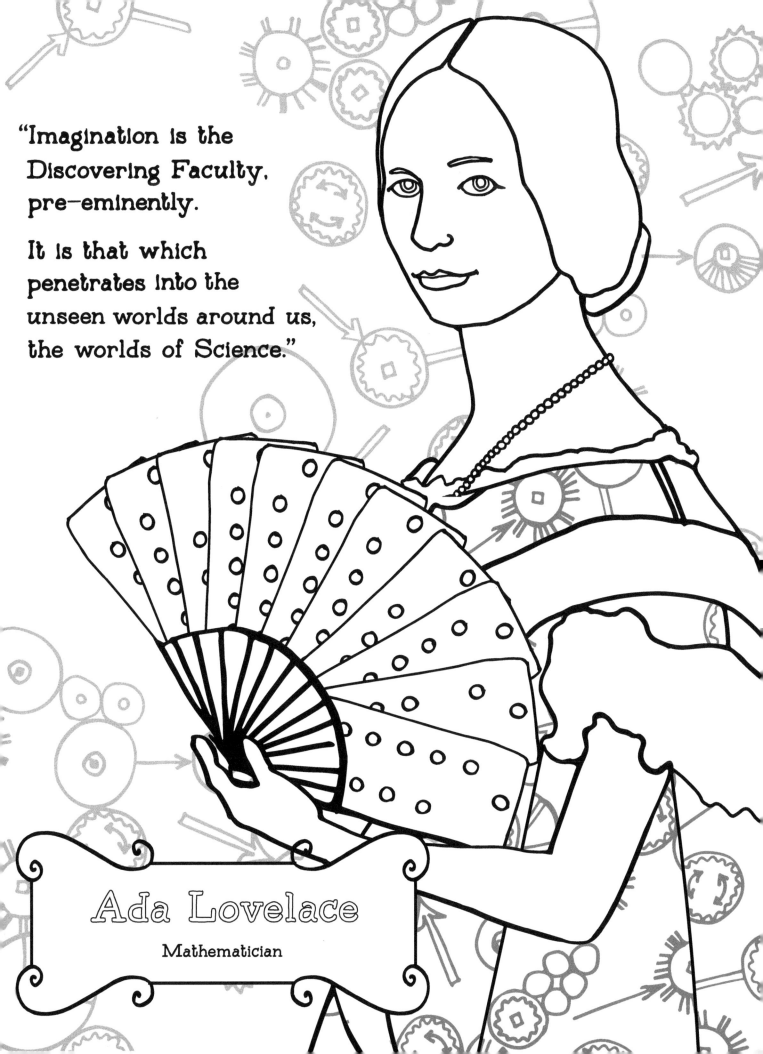

"Imagination is the Discovering Faculty, pre-eminently.

It is that which penetrates into the unseen worlds around us, the worlds of Science."

Ada Lovelace

Mathematician

Alice Ball

1892–1916

Alice Ball was born in 1892 in Seattle, Washington. She had a keen interest in science starting as early as high school. Alice co-published an article in the *Journal of the American Chemical Society* while working on her undergraduate degree in chemistry. She went on to receive a master's degree in chemistry from the University of Hawai'i — becoming the first African American woman and also the first woman at all to accomplish this.

Upon graduation Alice did both postgraduate research and teaching at the University of Hawai'i. She was then asked to assist Dr. Harry T. Hollmann of Kalihi Hospital in figuring out how to isolate the active chemical compounds in chaulmoogra oil. The oil, found in a tropical tree that comes from India, had been used to treat leprosy, taken by the mouth. Alice figured out how to isolate the compound so that it could be given to leprosy patients through injection.

Unfortunately, she died before she could publish her research. Another chemist, Arthur Dean, not only continued her research and published it, but he did not give Alice any credit. In 1922 her former colleague Dr. Hollmann brought attention to this great disservice. Her method for isolating the active chemical compound was used until the 1940s. In the year 2000, a bronze plaque commemorating her work was placed at the University of Hawai'i's only chaulmoogra tree, the very one Alice had used to extract the oil.

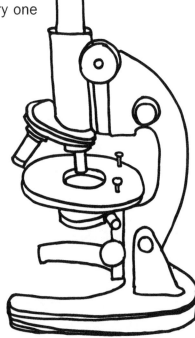

Alice Ball

Chemist

Amalie Emmy Noether

1882–1935

Emmy Noether was born into a Jewish family of scientists in Erlangen, Germany in 1882. At first, because of her gender, she could only audit classes in mathematics. It wasn't until 1907 that she was finally allowed to receive her Ph.D. on algebraic invariants from the University of Erlangen, but even with that she was not able to get a paid position because she was a woman. She worked, unpaid, at the Mathematical Institute of Erlangen from 1908 to 1915. When Emmy fled to the United States in 1933 because of religious persecution by Nazi Germany, she was finally given a paid position at Bryn Mawr College.

Despite these enormous obstacles, Emmy persevered and one of her mathematical theorems is considered one of the most important in **theoretical physics**. In fact, her theorem even helped to solve a problem in Albert Einstein's **general theory of relativity**! Some of her other work profoundly changed the appearance of algebra which concluded with a published paper in 1920.

Because of Emmy's many contributions to mathematics, she inspired many successors in what became known as the "Noether School" of mathematics. In 1932 she received the Ackermann-Teubner Memorial Award, and both a crater on the Moon and a minor planet are named for Emmy.

Amalie Emmy Noether

Mathematician

Anna Atkins

1799–1871

Anna Atkins was born in Tonbridge, England, in 1799. Her father, John George Children, was a **botanist** at the British Museum of Natural History and a Fellow of the Royal Society of London. He encouraged Anna's own interests in science. Early in her life, Anna created 200 illustrations for her father's translation of Jean-Baptiste Lamarck's *Genera of Shells* (1823).

However, Anna's passion lay beyond illustrating. She was the first person to use the newly invented cyanotype process (an early type of photography) to scientifically document **algae**, plants, and ferns. This new form of light-sensitive documentation worked by placing an object onto paper and exposing it to sunlight. Since the paper was treated with various chemicals, the area not covered by the object would turn a dark blue. Anna self-published *Photographs of British Algae: Cyanotype Impressions* (1843), in which she documented all of the known algae (seaweed) specimens of the British Isles. It is perhaps the first book that utilized photographic images.

She later collaborated with her childhood friend Anne Dixon, a fellow botanist and photographer, to publish *Cyanotypes of British and Foreign Ferns* (1853) and *Cyanotypes of British and Foreign Flowering Plants and Ferns* (1854). Anna became a member of the Botanical Society of London in 1839.

Anna Atkins

Botanist

Anna Botsford Comstock

1854–1930

Anna Botsford Comstock, born on a farm in Otto, New York in 1854, was encouraged by her parents to explore nature. This early exposure to the benefits of being out in natural surroundings led her to pursue a degree in natural history from Cornell University, which she completed in 1885. With the support of her husband, John Henry Comstock, an entomology professor at Cornell, Anna devoted her life to raising awareness on the importance of hands-on exploration and observation of nature.

Her dedication to nature education resulted in receiving an assistantship in nature study at Cornell in 1897. She helped launch a nature study program in Westchester County, New York that later became a nation-wide program along with lecturing on the topic around the country. She published a guide for teachers in 1911 called *Handbook of Nature Study*, which included her own wood engraving illustrations. It was her hope to explain and encourage an understanding of why the direct observation of nature was so important for children. It was also her hope to help teachers "cultivate the child's imagination, love of the beautiful, and sense of companionship with life out-of-doors."

She published many other books, including *Ways of the Six-Footed* (1903), *How to Keep Bees* (1905), and *Trees at Leisure* (1916). She also edited the American Nature Study Society's journal *The Nature Study Review* from 1908 to 1923, taking it upon herself to publish the journal from 1917 to 1923 under her and her husband's own press, Comstock Publishing Company. She became an assistant professor in 1899, but was demoted to "lecturer" as not everyone at Cornell liked the idea of a woman holding a professorship. She was later reinstated in 1913, and made full professor in 1920.

Anna was honored by the League of Women Voters in 1923 as one of "twelve living women who have contributed in their respective fields to the betterment of the world." Her *Handbook of Nature Study* remains in print today and is used by teachers and families that instill in their students and children a love of nature.

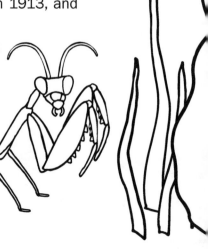

Anna Botsford Comstock

Naturalist and Educator

Annie Jump Cannon

1863–1941

Annie Jump Cannon, the "Census Taker of the Sky," was born in 1863 in Dover, Delaware, where in the attic of their family home her mother taught her the **constellations** with a makeshift observatory. This experience ignited her passion for the sky, inspiring her to study both physics and astronomy at Wellesley College, followed by further studies in astronomy at Radcliffe College.

In 1896 Annie became an assistant at the Harvard College Observatory on Edward Pickering's team of "computers," a group of women, including Henrietta Swan Leavitt, that organized astronomical data and ran calculations. While there, she developed a classification system for stars that is still used today. Annie simplified the system that was then in use and applied it to the whole survey of stars across the sky (the system divided stars into the spectral classes of O, B, A, F, G, K, and M, with O being the hottest and M being the coolest). Her work on this, published with Edward Pickering as *The Henry Draper Catalogue* (1918-24) and *The Henry Draper Extension* (1925–49), contained the classification of 350,000 stars!

Despite these immense accomplishments, due to gender discrimination, it took 40 years for Annie to finally obtain professorship at Harvard. Her contributions were so important that she was the first woman elected as an officer of the American Astronomical Society. As a suffragist, she used her own prize money to establish a fund — the "Annie Jump Cannon Award in Astronomy," which is still given by the American Astronomical Society every year to a woman who has received her Ph.D. no more than five years prior. Annie even has a Moon crater and an asteroid named after her.

Study Annie's system below.
Can you identify and label the stars on this page?

Annie
Jump Cannon

Astronomer

Beatrix Potter

1866–1943

Beatrix Potter was born into a wealthy Victorian family in London in 1866. As a child, she spent her free time painting and observing a wide variety of pets and animals, including rabbits, mice, a hedgehog, squirrels, lizards, and a bat. She would even draw the bones of animals when she had them available. Beatrix was the epitome of a self-taught naturalist! Although her family saw no need in her having an education beyond that of what her governess provided, Beatrix was fortunate to frequent the British Museum's natural history collections. She was even introduced to a working artist, who inspired her to continue working on her own illustration and watercolor techniques.

While her brother attended University, Beatrix continued to practice her observation and painting. On a trip to the Scottish countryside, she became awestruck with **fungi** (mushrooms). She went on to illustrate 300 drawings of specimens and recorded her observations in a journal. With the encouragement of her uncle and under the mentorship of mycologist Charles McIntosh, Beatrix prepared a paper on her observations of the symbiotic relationship between **algae** and fungi in **lichen**. However, due to her gender, she was not allowed to read her paper to the Linnean Society of London — a man had to read it for her. Her heart broken from not being able to truly practice science, Beatrix turned toward her talents for illustration and storytelling, creating one of the best known children's series in the world — *The Tale of Peter Rabbit*.

Her stories were such a success that she was able to buy 4,000 acres of land that included 15 farms in the Lake District of England. She turned her attention to sheep farming in her later years. Upon her death, she donated all of her property for conservation purposes to the National Trust. Today, her watercolor drawings of fungi are properly recognized for their accuracy and are even used by experts to identify rare species.

Beatrix was famous for her watercolors in stories and in science. Can you use her watercolor set below to paint her portrait on the right?

Beatrix Potter

Naturalist and Scientific Illustrator

Caroline Herschel

1750–1848

Caroline Herschel was born in 1750 in Hanover, Germany, to a father who felt his children should have an education. Her mother disagreed, however, and took every chance she had to make Caroline do house work. Due to the severity of an illness Caroline suffered as a child, her growth was stunted, deeming her destined to be a spinster. Dissatisfied with such a limited destiny, she went with her brother William Herschel to England, where he taught her music and mathematics while sharing a love for star-gazing.

In William's free time and with the help of Caroline, they constructed what would become the most powerful telescope available. William's career took a full turn towards astronomy after he discovered a new planet (Uranus). Although Caroline assisted William, she also took every spare moment she had to observe the night sky herself — discovering three new **nebulae** and eight **comets** — becoming one of the first women to discover a comet!

In 1787 Caroline was granted a salary and later produced the *Catalogue of Stars*, which contained an index to "every observation of every star made by Flamsteed" (Britain's first Astronomer Royal). In 1828 she was the first woman to be awarded a Gold Medal of the Royal Astronomical Society and in 1835 to be named an Honorary Member of the Royal Astronomical Society (along with Mary Somerville).

"The eyes of her who is glorified here below turned to the starry heavens."

Caroline Herschel

Astronomer

Dorothea Bate

1878–1951

Dorothea Bate was born in 1878 in Carmarthen, South Wales. With her father's encouragement of collecting natural artifacts coupled with their move to Gloucester, where she explored the area's many caves, Dorothea became fascinated with **paleontology**. Her passion for the subject paid off when she impressed the curator of the British Museum's Bird Room with her knowledge of bird **taxonomy**. However, since no woman at that time could have a paid position at the museum, she became a volunteer.

In 1902, while exploring the caves of Cyprus, she discovered the fossilized remains of pygmy elephants. Her work later led her to become the leading authority on Pleistocene avian and mammalian faunas of Cyprus, Crete, the Balearic Islands, England, Corsica, Sardinia, Israel, and Sweden. Dorothea also became the go-to person on topics of Mediterranean island **vertebrate** fossils, for in her explorations of Mediterranean island caves, she discovered fossil remains of a deer (*Candiacervus*), a rodent (*Mus minotaurus*), dwarf elephants new to science (*Elephas cypriotes* and *Elephas creticus*), a dwarf hippo (*Hippopotamus minutus*), a dormouse (*Hypnomys Morpheus*), and the "mouse goat" (*Myotragus balearicus*).

Dorothea published some eighty works on natural history subjects and even studied with the famous anthropologist Louis Leakey. She was finally granted a paid position, at the age of 70, at the Natural History Museum of Tring, a satellite of the main museum in London.

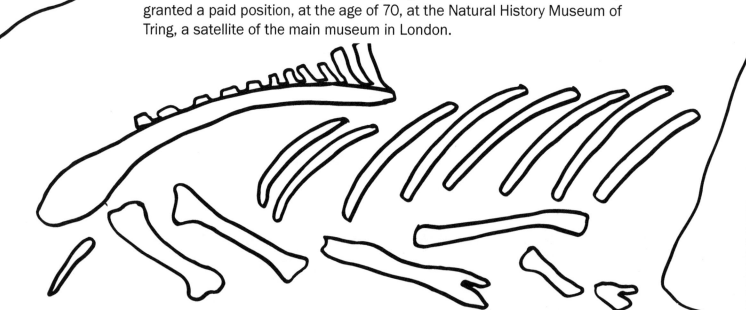

Dorothea Bate

Vertebrate Paleontologist
and Archaeozoologist

"The quality of life depends on the ability of society to teach its members how to live in harmony with their environment."

Ellen Swallow Richards

1842–1911

Ellen Swallow Richards, born in Dunstable, Massachusetts in 1842, was the daughter to schoolteacher parents who valued education. While assisting her father at their village shop, Ellen observed the buying habits of women. This led to her interest in issues of product purity as well as air and water contamination. She went on to attend the newly opened institution for women, Vassar College. Although she enjoyed her classes with astronomy teacher Maria Mitchell, Ellen decided to pursue **chemistry** for its more useful applications in what interested her the most — **ecology**, **home economics** and **sanitation**.

Ellen became the first woman in America to graduate with a degree in chemistry and the first woman to be accepted to a school of science — the Massachusetts Institute of Technology. She would have earned her doctoral degree in chemistry from MIT, but the school refused to be the first to give a woman a Ph.D.

Ellen felt passionately that women should have equal opportunities to learn science and helped establish the Woman's Laboratory at MIT and was a co-founder of the American Association of University Women. While at the Woman's Laboratory she became the first woman instructor — teaching other women in sanitary chemistry and biology, for instance. She published a number of books on both sanitation and home economics and helped to establish the *Journal of Home Economics*. Ellen even used her own home as a lab — which she named the "Center for Right Living" — to test everyday items such as food, milk, water, and air for health and safety purposes. Some of her research showed that mahogany sawdust was found in cinnamon and sand in sugar! This revelation led the government of Massachusetts to officially start monitoring food and medicine.

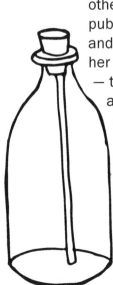

As a founding ecofeminist, Ellen worked toward raising awareness of the well-being of housewives and the importance of their work at home for the economy. Her own home and her lab in Boston are now National Historic Landmarks.

Ellen
Swallow Richards
Chemist and Home Economist

Émilie du Châtelet

1706–1749

Émilie du Châtelet was born into a family of nobility in 1706, in Paris, France. While it was incredibly uncommon for girls to be educated at this time, Émilie's father recognized how bright she was and sought out tutors in astronomy, mathematics, literature, science, Latin, Greek, German, and Italian. Her father also hosted a weekly *salon*, a time when writers and scientists would gather to discuss their ideas. Émilie was exposed quite early and quite unconventionally to some of the greatest minds of the time.

Although she was married to Florent-Claude, marquis du Châtelet (in 1725), Émilie later fell in love with the prominent French philosopher Voltaire. They shared their interests in science, at times working together at her home-lab. Voltaire introduced her to Isaac Newton's work on the **laws of mechanical physics**, which would lead to her biggest contribution to the scientific community: a French translation (from Latin) and commentary of Newton's *Philosophiae Naturalis Principia Mathematica*, also known as the *Principia*. She completed this in the 1740s, but died in 1749 and it was not published in complete form until 1756. It remains the standard translation in use today. Émilie also wrote papers and books, including *Dissertation sur la Nature et la Propagation du Feu* (1739) and *Institutions de Physique* (1740), in which she reconciled the conflicting ideas of Newton's mechanics and philosopher Gottfried Leibniz's **metaphysics**.

Émilie is remembered today for her contributions in synthesizing and popularizing scientific ideas, and her life-story, full of drama and conflict, has been made into three separate plays as well as an opera. A minor planet and a crater on Venus are both named in her honor.

"I'm convinced that most women are either ignorant of their talents, or they cover them up. Everything I've experienced myself confirms this opinion."

Émilie du Châtelet
Mathematician and Writer on Natural Philosophy

Genevieve Jones

1847-1879

Genevieve Jones was born in 1847 in Circleville, Ohio. Her father Nelson was a physician, with whom Genevieve would often travel on house calls in order to help him collect bird nests and eggs for their personal collection of natural history items. One day she discovered a nest that neither her amateur ornithologist father or her younger brother Howard could identify. Genevieve in turn felt determined to find a book that would identify their finding. She was stunned to discover that no such book existed!

In 1876 Genevieve visited the Centennial International Exhibition in Philadelphia, where she viewed an exhibit of John James Audubon's monumental *The Birds of America*. Between viewing his beautiful lithographs and realizing his lack of proper documentation of bird eggs and their nests, she felt inspired to create a book. With her family supporting her, she began illustrating 130 species of bird eggs and nests in Ohio. Her brother helped search for the specimens and her parents organized the necessary steps to publish the book, setting it up as a subscription. Two of the subscribers included former President Rutherford B. Hayes and a natural history buff, Theodore Roosevelt (then a student at Harvard). Genevieve received praise when the first prints were sent out to subscribers, comparing her work to and above that of Audubon.

Quite tragically, Genevieve would never see her two-volume *Illustrations of the Nests and Eggs of Birds of Ohio* come to fruition. She died from typhoid fever in 1879 after having completed only five of the species. Her family took over the project in her honor, her mother Virginia illustrating, her brother writing the text, and her father financing the project. After seven years of painstaking work, it was finished. However, the completed work was really too expensive for people to purchase. A family copy of the book was eventually given to the Cleveland Museum of Natural History, where later in the twentieth century a librarian came upon it and has since published an edition of the book for folks to learn about this beautiful work of American natural history.

Genevieve Jones

Botanical Illustrator and Naturalist

Henrietta Swan Leavitt

1868–1921

Henrietta Swan Leavitt was born in Lancaster, Massachusetts in 1868. It wasn't until her senior year in college, at what is now Radcliffe College, that she took an astronomy class. She loved the class so much that she took another astronomy course after graduation and then volunteered as one of the women "computers" for Edward Pickering at the Harvard College Observatory, along with Annie Jump Cannon.

In 1902 she was appointed to a permanent position — chief of the photographic **photometry** department — at the Observatory and remained there until her death in 1921. Her work encompassed studying 1,777 stars on photographic plates, and her research on the brightness of these stars became known as Leavitt's Law.

This discovery was later instrumental in Edwin Hubble determining that the universe was expanding, and because of this he stated she should receive the Nobel Prize! Unfortunately it was too late, for she had died a few years earlier. Both an asteroid and a crater on the Moon are named in her honor.

Henrietta Swan Leavitt

Astronomer

Hertha Marks Ayrton

1854–1923

Hertha Ayrton was born Phoebe Sarah Marks in 1854 in Portsea, England. After her father died in 1861, she moved to London to attend a school run by her aunt. Hertha's mother was unsupportive of a girl receiving an education, so this opportunity to be schooled dramatically changed her life. She went on to attend Girton College at the University of Cambridge, where she studied mathematics.

In 1884 Hertha invented a line dividing tool, best used by architects for drafting. This was just one of twenty-six patents registered in her name. Shortly thereafter, she attended classes on electricity at Finsbury Technical School, where she met her future husband, electrical engineer and professor William Ayrton. Hertha went on to discover the cause of hissing in the electric arc of arc lamps and presented her paper to the Institution of Electrical Engineers, becoming not only the first woman to do so, but also the first female member of the organization. However, when she desired to read her paper "The Mechanism of the Electric Arc" before the Royal Society of London in 1901, she was not permitted to because of her gender. Instead, a man read it in her place. That same man later pushed to have Hertha made a Fellow of the Royal Society but she was denied, again, on account of her gender.

This discrimination did not stop Hertha — she continued to see science everywhere! While spending time at the seaside, she became curious about how ripples were formed in the sand. Hertha took that opportunity to conduct experiments in **hydrodynamics**, and in 1904 she read her paper "The Origin and Growth of Ripple-mark" before the Royal Society, becoming the first woman to do so. In 1906, the Royal Society awarded Hertha their Hughes Medal for her research on electric arcs and sand-ripples. Her book, *The Electric Arc* (1902), became the standard textbook on the subject.

Engineer tip!

A vortex occurs due to a disturbance in flow and results in the fluid moving in a rotation like eddies in a stream and whirlpools in a boat's wake. Vortices result from turbulence.

Hertha Marks Ayrton

Mathemetician, Physicist, Inventor, and Engineer

Inge Lehmann

1888–1993

Inge Lehmann was born in 1888 in Copenhagen, Denmark, where she spent her entire life dedicated to the study of **seismology**. She received two master's degrees from the University of Copenhagen, one in 1920 in mathematics and physics and another in 1928 in **geodesy**. In 1925 Inge became most interested in studying seismology, propelling her to become the chief of the seismological department at the Danish Geodetic Institute from 1928 to 1953. She traveled the world supervising the installation of seismographs stations that were used to capture data from seismic waves created by earthquakes or explosions that traveled through the earth. Since certain types of waves responded differently according to the material they passed through, researchers could theorize and determine what made up the earth's interior.

Inge proposed in 1936 that the earth was in fact made up of two parts — a solid inner core and a liquid outer core. This theory would only decades later be confirmed once more accurate seismograph readings were taken. To this day some of the boundaries between layers within the earth are referred to as "Lehmann discontinuities."

Inge was a founding member of the Danish Geophysical Association and a member of numerous other scientific societies, including being a foreign member of the Royal Society of London. She published over fifty-six scientific papers. In 1996, the American Geophysical Union created an annual Inge Lehmann Medal to acknowledge "outstanding contributions toward the understanding of the structure, composition and/or dynamics of the Earth's mantle and core."

Inge Lehmann

Geologist

Jeanne Baré

1740–1807

Jeanne Baré, born in France in 1740 to a peasant family, grew up learning how to use plants to treat wounds and diseases. She initially worked as a housekeeper for the French botanist Philibert Commerson. Their relationship morphed over the years — changing Jeanne's life forever. Not only did Commerson appreciate Jeanne's help as a researcher, but she helped care for his various illnesses.

In 1766, Commerson had the opportunity to join the Bougainville expedition on the ships *La Boudeuse* and *Étoile*. However, because the French Navy forbade woman from sailing on such expeditions, Commerson and Jeanne decided to disguise herself as a man, "Jean Baret," in order to join the expedition as Commerson's assistant. It was this voyage that began her historic trip — making her the first woman to circumnavigate the globe!

Together, Commerson and Jeanne collected over 6,000 plant specimens in just two years. One of their discoveries included the now universally beloved flowering plant *Bougainvillea*. Because of Commerson's ill health, Jeanne did a lot of the the physical labor herself — traversing foreign terrains, exploring, and hauling finds back to the ship. To honor Jeanne, Commerson had named a plant after her, but the name never became official.

When it became known that "Jean" was truly a woman, she and Commerson disembarked to finish their botany research in Mauritius, an island in the Indian Ocean also known as the "Isle de France." Eventually Jeanne made it back to France, where her contributions to the field of botany were recognized and she was awarded an annual government pension. In 2012, a new plant species, *Solanum baretiae*, was named for Jeanne by biologist Eric Tepe.

Botanist tip!

The brightly colored blooms on bougainvillea aren't actually flowers. They are called **bracts**. Three to six brachts surround the flowers, which are very small and white and found in the middle of the bract.

bract

flower

Jeanne Baré

Botanist and Explorer

Jeanne Villepreux-Power
1794–1871

Jeanne Villepreux-Power, "the Mother of **Aquariophily**," was born in 1794 in Juillac, France. The daughter of a shoemaker, Jeanne traveled to Paris to pursue dress-making. She became quite successful! At the age of 24, Jeanne moved to Sicily to begin a new life with her husband. It was there that she became fascinated with natural history. Jeanne was interested in both **marine** and **terrestrial** animals, but mostly in **mollusks** and their **fossils**. Frustrated that she couldn't easily study marine life in a controlled setting, she used her extraordinary creativity to invent three types of aquariums. One design most resembles what we know today — complete with a glass enclosure. The other two had the capability of being submerged in water.

With her new inventions, Jeanne took it upon herself to inventory the life of the Sicilian coast (Mediterranean Sea). She spent over ten years observing and studying the *Argonauta argo* (a species of octopus, called greater argonaut or paper nautilus) and discovered that they did in fact create their own shell. In 1839 Jeanne published a book about her experiments, *Observations et Expériences Physiques sur Plusieurs Animaux Marins et Terrestres* (*Physical Observations and Experiments on Several Marine and Terrestrial Animals*), and in 1842 she published *Guida per la Sicilia* (*Guide to Sicily*). Sadly, most of her papers and scientific drawings were lost in a shipwreck between Paris and London — and she then discontinued her research in natural history. In 1997, a crater on the planet Venus was named in her honor.

Jeanne
Villepreux-Power

Marine Biologist

Lise Meitner

1878–1968

Lise Meitner was born in Vienna, Austria in 1878 to wonderfully supportive parents. She was an inquisitive child and at the age of eight was already conducting her own research. This encouraged Lise's parents to provide her with the education she wanted and needed to best support her innate talents.

In 1906 Lise became the second woman to receive a doctoral degree in physics from the University of Vienna. With the financial backing of her father, she moved to Berlin, Germany to attend lectures by Max Planck at Friedrich-Wilhelms-Universität. In 1919, Lise became the first woman to work as a professor of physics in Germany at the Kaiser Wilhelm Institute. Unfortunately, in the 1930s she had to flee Nazi-controlled Germany to Sweden due to her Jewish heritage. She persevered however and continued her research and work in Sweden, and eventually became a Swedish citizen in 1949.

While she accomplished much in **nuclear physics**, and was friends with many eminent physicists (Albert Einstein included), Lise is best known for her work with chemist Otto Hahn in the splitting of the uranium atom (called **nuclear fission**, a process instrumental in the development of atomic weapons). However, she was not recognized for her work when only Hahn was awarded the 1944 Nobel Prize in Chemistry. Lise's contributions were monumental and since then the worldwide scientific community has continued to honor her work. Several university awards in physics are named in her honor, as well as craters on the Moon and on Venus and an asteroid. In 1997, element 109 was named meitnerium. Later in life, Lise advocated for world peace and the control of nuclear weapons.

Lise Meitner

Physicist

Maria Emma Gray

1787–1879

Maria Emma Gray, born in 1787 in London, had an early interest in both science and literature. After her first husband died, she befriended his cousin, John Gray, an assistant in the natural history department of the British Museum. They would marry, and their union allowed Maria the opportunity to pursue her own passion for natural history.

Over the course of thirty years, from 1842 to 1874, Maria etched thousands of marine animal plates for the five-volume series *Figures of Molluscous Animals*. With her interest in **mollusks** and **algae**, she arranged the collection and mounted a display of shells at the British Museum and arranged the collection of British algae at Kew Gardens.

Maria was of great assistance to John's own scientific work, yet she was never properly given credit due to her gender. John did, however, name a new species of algae in her honor in 1866, *Grayemma*, as well as two species of lizard, *Calotes maria* and *Calotes emma*.

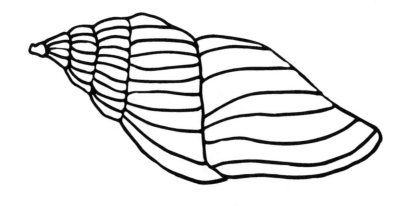

Maria
Emma Gray

Botanist

Maria Sibylla Merian

1647–1717

Maria Sibylla Merian was born in Frankfurt, Germany in 1647. Both her father, a renowned artist and engraver, and then her step-father, a still-life painter, greatly influenced her love of art and interest in insects. At a young age, she collected caterpillars and even documented the stages of their **metamorphoses**.

These formative experiences inspired Maria to publish *Der Raupen wunderbare Verwendung und sonderbare Blumen-nahrung* (*Wonderful Transformation and Special Nourishment of Caterpillars*) in 1679, which described the life cycle of caterpillar species in incredible detail and scientific accuracy. Her work was so impressive that when she moved to Amsterdam to be more involved in the scientific community, she was hired to prepare 127 illustrations for a French translation of Johann Goedart's *Metamorphisis et History Naturalis Insectorum*.

In 1699, Maria was awarded a grant by the Dutch government to spend five years in Surinam, alone with her daughter, to both search for and scientifically study exotic plants and insects. When they returned to Amsterdam, she published her illustrated book, *Metamorphosis Insectorum Surinamensium* (*The Metamorphosis of the Insects of Suriname*), that detailed the development of native insects. It was one of the first books that documented the natural history of Surinam. Maria's scientific achievements were honored, in 1991, when Germany put her portrait on the 500 Deutsche Mark banknote.

Maria Sibylla Merian

Naturalist, Entomologist, and Botanical Artist

Maria Mitchell

1818–1889

Maria Mitchell was born to a large Quaker family in 1818 on the island of Nantucket in Massachusetts. An important belief in the Quaker religion was that men and women should be given equal educational opportunities. Maria's father even opened a school at which she eventually became a student and assistant. At home he taught her astronomy and together they would study the stars with his telescope. When Maria was twelve, she and her father observed a **solar eclipse** and used it to calculate the position of their home. She even briefly opened her own school that was accepting of non-white children, unconventional at the time. Maria went on to be a librarian at the Nantucket Atheneum for two decades.

In 1847, Maria discovered a comet with the use of her telescope that was named "Miss Mitchell's Comet." She was the third woman to ever discover a comet (after Caroline Herschel and Maria Margarethe Kirch of Germany). Her discovery resulted in her receiving a gold medal prize from King Frederick VI of Denmark.

Maria was the first professional woman astronomer in the United States, working as a professor of astronomy at Vassar College in New York from 1865 until just a year before her death in 1889. She was the first woman elected to the American Academy of Arts and Sciences as well as the American Association for the Advancement of Science. Maria was also a believer in equal rights for women (co-founding the American Association for the Advancement of Women) and protested against slavery.

In 1902 the Maria Mitchell Association was founded to preserve her legacy. Located on Nantucket, the association oversees two observatories, a natural history museum, an aquarium, and her home. Maria was also inducted into the US National Women's Hall of Fame.

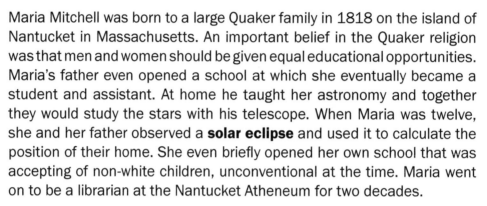
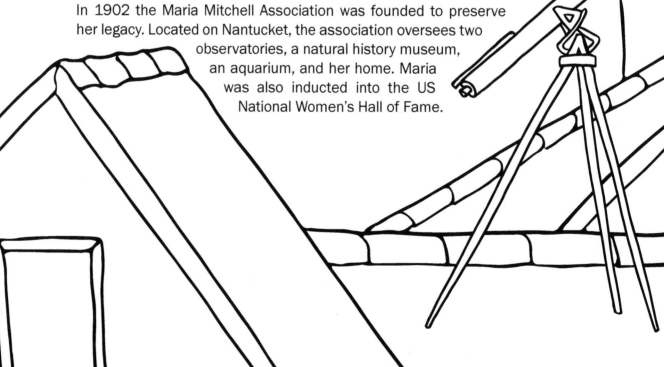

"We especially need imagination in science. It is not all logic, nor all mathematics, but is somewhat beauty and poetry."
—Maria Mitchell

Maria Mitchell

Astronomer

Marie Curie & Irène Joliot-Curie

1867–1934 & 1897–1956

Marie Curie, born to well educated parents in 1867 in Warsaw, Poland, sought a life that would provide her with an education in physics and mathematics. Her perseverance paid off when by 1894 she had obtained degrees in physics and mathematics. One year later she married Pierre Curie, a laboratory chief at the School of Industrial Physics and Chemistry in Paris, France.

After publishing her first paper the very year (1897) her daughter Irène was born, Marie decided that she wanted to learn more about **radioactivity** (a word she coined herself!) for her doctoral dissertation at the University of Paris. Not only did Marie develop the theory of radioactivity, but it was during this research that she discovered two new elements: polonium and radium. Marie, her husband, and Henri Becquerel were jointly awarded the Nobel Prize for Physics in 1903, making Marie the first woman to win one. She would again be awarded the Nobel Prize in 1911, this time for Chemistry, becoming the only person in history to win for two separate sciences! Marie was also the first woman in France to become a professor at the University of Paris.

With such a perceptive mother as Marie, her daughter Irène was given a particularly incredible education. Once Irène's own talent for mathematics was recognized, Marie organized an elite group of scientists and scholars to form "The Cooperative" in which they would teach each other's children. After two years, Irène went on to traditional education. Unfortunately, World War I halted Irène's plan to finish college. It was not until 1925 when she finally earned her doctoral degree upon returning to college. During the war, Irène helped her mother at a number of field hospitals as a nurse radiographer, using vehicles with **x-ray** devices (of Marie's own design) to help doctors better locate shrapnel in wounded soldiers. Marie died in 1934 due to the heavy exposure to **radiation** she endured during her lifetime.

Back in Paris and working at her parents' *Institut Curie* (founded in 1909), Irène and her husband, Frédéric Joliot-Curie, a chemical engineer, continued research on the elements her parents had discovered. Together they figured out how to turn one element into another. This discovery of induced (artificial) radioactivity was so profound that Irène and Frédéric were awarded a Nobel Prize in Chemistry in 1935! She was also given professorship at the Faculty of Science in Paris.

The Curie family is one of the most well-known in science and is the most awarded family in history with five Nobel Prizes! Even the children of Irène and Frédéric became accomplished scientists.

Mary Anning

1799–1847

Mary Anning was born in the town of Lyme Regis in southern coastal England in 1799. From the time she was a child, she was destined to become a renowned fossil hunter. Her father, a cabinetmaker by trade, collected fossils both as a hobby and to sell as a means to support his family. Even at a young age, Mary would stand outside at their family table, selling fossils. And certainly at the time of her father's death in 1810, she persevered, stepping right into his shoes, collecting fossils to sell at her own table beside a local inn, to help support her family.

It was at this time Mary and her brother made a huge discovery — a complete *Ichthyosaurus* skeleton. Although she was not given credit for the finding, it amassed a great deal of attention by scientists, followed by publication of an official description in 1817.

Her passion and self-taught skills for finding fossils persisted. Mary discovered a complete specimen of *Plesiosaurus* in 1823, a *Pterodactylus* skeleton in 1828, and later a fossil fish and a specimen of a new species of plesiosaur named *Plesiosaurus marcocephalus*. By 1826 she was able to purchase her own home, complete with a storefront window. Mary opened up shop — Anning's Fossil Depot. This was a pivotal time in humanity's understanding of the history of life on earth and Mary's discoveries played a large part in the development of a new concept called **extinction**. Prominent geologists and paleontologists frequented her shop and even went fossil hunting with her.

Today, the Lyme Regis Museum celebrates Mary Anning Day every year and several fossil findings have been named in her honor, including *Acrodus anningiae*, *Belenostomus anningiae*, the plesiosaur *Anningasaura*, and *Ichthyosaurus anningae*.

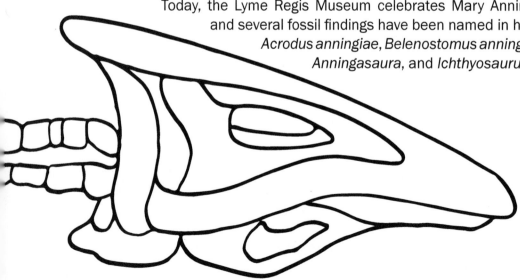

ANNING'S FOSSIL DEPOT

Mary Anning

Paleontologist

Mary Somerville

1780–1872

Mary Somerville was born in 1780 in Scotland. Although her father believed enough in the right of his daughter to have an education, he was not supportive of her learning mathematics. She not only taught herself Greek, but she also studied Euclid's *Elements* and Bonnycastle's *Algebra* in private.

Mary's first husband, like her father, was also unsupportive of her intellectual interests. It wasn't until Mary met her second husband that she could finally pursue her fascination and talent for science and mathematics. Mary wrote a number of papers about experiments with **solar rays** and is most known for her ability to communicate science in a way that both the public and students could understand. Some of the books she published include *On the Connexion of the Physical Sciences*, *Physical Geography*, and *On Molecular and Microscopic Science*.

Because of her achievements and thanks to William Whewell, the term "scientist" was created to include her — a woman — since "man of science" was no longer appropriate! Mary was among the first women to become an honorary member of the Royal Astronomical Society (along with Caroline Herschel). You can see her papers and letters at the Bodleian Library of Oxford University and as of 2017, Mary will appear on the Royal Bank of Scotland's £10 note.

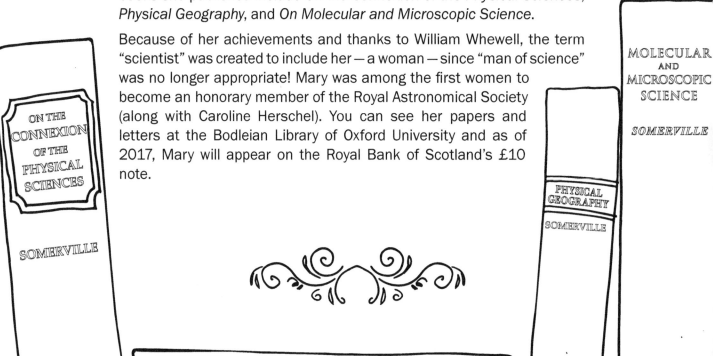

"Sometimes I find [mathematical problems] difficult, but my old obstinacy remains, for if I do not succeed today, I attack them again on the morrow."

Mary Somerville
Science Writer

Mary Treat

1830–1923

Mary Treat was born in 1830 in New York, but was mostly raised in Ohio. Although she attended schools as a girl, she was self-taught in the methods of natural history. In 1863 she married Dr. Joseph Burrell Treat who had many interests in science. Encouraged by this relationship, Mary pursued her own interests in botany and entomology.

Mary made numerous discoveries, including a new species of ant (*Aphanogaster treatiae*) and a new species of the flower amaryllis (*Zephyranthus treatiae*). She is known for her correspondence with the naturalists Charles Darwin and Asa Gray, and the entomologists Auguste Forel and Gustav Mayr. Darwin even acknowledged her contribution in his book, *Insectivorous Plants* (1875): "Mrs. Treat of New Jersey has been more successful than any other observer."

Over her lifetime, she wrote over 75 articles and five books. Her book *Injurious Insects of the Farm and Field* (1882) was reprinted five times. She died at her home in Vineland, New Jersey in 1923. Some of her work is available for viewing at the Vineland Historical and Antiquarian Society as well as at the Harvard University Herbaria in Cambridge, Massachusetts.

Mary Treat

Botanist and Entomologist

Nettie Stevens

1861–1912

Nettie Stevens, born in 1861 in Vermont, had a fascination with science and mathematics from an early age. She spent thirteen years as a schoolteacher and librarian before pursuing both a bachelor's and a master's degree from Stanford University. Her focus of study was in **histology**, the study of the microscopic structure of tissues.

Nettie then worked on a doctoral degree at Bryn Mawr College, where she became interested in how sex (male or female) was determined in organisms. Working with the common mealworm (the larval form of a beetle), she discovered that the egg cells of the female contained 20 large **chromosomes**, while the male sperm cells only had 19. She then concluded that sex was determined by the size difference of a single pair of chromosomes. It had previously been thought that sex was determined by the environment during development or through hereditary factors. Nettie's breakthrough was described in her 1905 paper "Studies in Spermatogenesis with Especial Reference to the 'Accessory Chromosome.'"

Unfortunately, historically credit for this discovery has been given to her Bryn Mawr colleague, biologist Edmund Beecher Wilson. Although it has since been proven that their studies were independent from one another and that her work was in fact pioneering, today Nettie still doesn't get the credit she deserves. This was exemplified in biologist Calvin Bridges' 1916 paper in *Genetics*, in which he cited Nettie's work, only to refer to her as "Miss Stevens" and not her well earned title "Dr. Stevens." She published nearly forty papers throughout her career. Nettie died in 1912 of breast cancer before she could ever take the position as a research professor that was created just for her at Bryn Mawr College.

Nettie Stevens

Geneticist

Roger Arliner Young

1889–1964

Roger Arliner Young was born in 1889 in Clifton Forge, Virginia, but was raised in Burgettstown, Pennsylvania. While her parents were uneducated, Roger strove to move beyond her upbringing by enrolling in college at Howard University. There she discovered her love for science. She assisted fellow African American zoologist and teacher Ernest Everett Just, graduating in 1923 with her own degree in zoology. While teaching as an assistant professor at Howard University, Roger attained her master's degree in zoology at the University of Chicago. In 1924 she became the first African American woman to publish a paper in the prestigious journal *Science*, "On the Excretory Apparatus in Paramecium."

For three years beginning in 1927 Roger assisted Just in research on ultraviolet radiation of marine invertebrate eggs at the Marine Biological Laboratories in Woods Hole, Massachusetts. Just never properly credited her with co-authorship of their published papers. However, Roger went on to publish several of her own original papers while working toward her PhD at the University of Pennsylvania. She rose above the challenges she faced throughout her career all while caring periodically for her ailing mother and while struggling with her own depression. She graduated with a doctorate degree in 1940.

Roger taught at several African American colleges around the country and participated in Civil Rights activism, specifically, by registering voters and organizing labor. In 2005 she was recognized in a **Congressional Resolution**, with four other African American women "who have broken through many barriers to achieve greatness in science."

Roger
Arliner Young

Zoologist

Sofia Kovalevskaya

1850–1891

Sofia Kovalevskaya was born in 1850 in Moscow, Russia to a long family line of scientists and military members, including her father, General Vasily Vasilyevich Korvin-Krukovsky. She was provided with a strong education from the start and showed particular talents in mathematics. Unfortunately, because Sofia was a woman, she was not permitted to attend university in Russia. So she left Russia to pursue further studies in Germany, where she was allowed to audit classes at the University of Heidelberg (however, in order to be permitted to leave Russia, she had to marry a man who was also heading to another country for education).

After studying in Heidleberg, Sofia moved on to studying privately with mathematician Karl Weierstrass as the university in Berlin would not allow her to sit in on lectures. It was under Weierstrass' tutelage that she wrote and presented three papers — one on elliptical integrals, another on Saturn's rings, and her most important paper on partial differential equations. This third paper, "On the Theory of Partial Differential Equations," impressed the European mathematical community, earning Sofia a doctoral degree, summa cum laude, from the University of Göttingen.

While Sofia was certainly credentialed in mathematics, she did not find a teaching position at a European university. She returned to Russia for a time, and then in 1883 was hired by Gosta Mittag-Leffler of the University of Stockholm as lecturer in mathematics (he was an acquaintance of Weierstrass). Sofia is best known for her paper from 1888, "On the Rotation of a Solid Body about a Fixed Point," which earned her as award from the French Academy of Sciences. Sofia later became the first woman to be elected as a member of the Russian Academy of Sciences. She also advocated for women's rights and shared her own experiences as a girl in Russia in her autobiography *Memories of Childhood* and a series of autobiographical novels, including *The University Lecturer* and *Nihilist Girl*.

Physicist tip!

A toy top spins due to the conservation of angular momentum which keeps it balanced on its tip while spinning at a high speed. As friction causes the top to slow down, it becomes unstable and begins to wobble before finally falling over.

"It seems to me that the poet has only to perceive that which others do not perceive, to look deeper than others look. And the mathematician must do the same thing."

Sofia Kovalevskaya

Mathematician

Wang Zhenyi

1768–1797

Wang Zhenyi (Chen-I) was born in 1768 in China during the Qing dynasty. With the support of her family, she broke with tradition and pursued her many academic interests, primarily astronomy and mathematics. Although she lived a short life, dying in 1797 at the age of 29, she made quite an impact.

Zhenyi was mostly self-taught and felt passionately about writing on the topics she loved in a manner that lay people could understand. She wrote several papers and books on mathematics and astronomy, including a book about the position of the stars called *Some Observations on Forms and Figures*. Another topic of her research was trigonometry and the Pythagorean theorem.

Most notably and quite ingeniously, Zhenyi set up models in her home by using a round table (as the Earth), a mirror (as the Moon), and a lamp (as the Sun) to accurately describe how **lunar and solar eclipses** work. She explained her work in the book *The Interpretation of the Eclipse of the Moon*. Zhenyi wrote 12 volumes on astronomy and mathematics, but unfortunately they have been lost to history.

"There were times I had to put down my pen and sigh. But I love the subject. I do not give up."

Wang Zhenyi

Mathematician and Astronomer

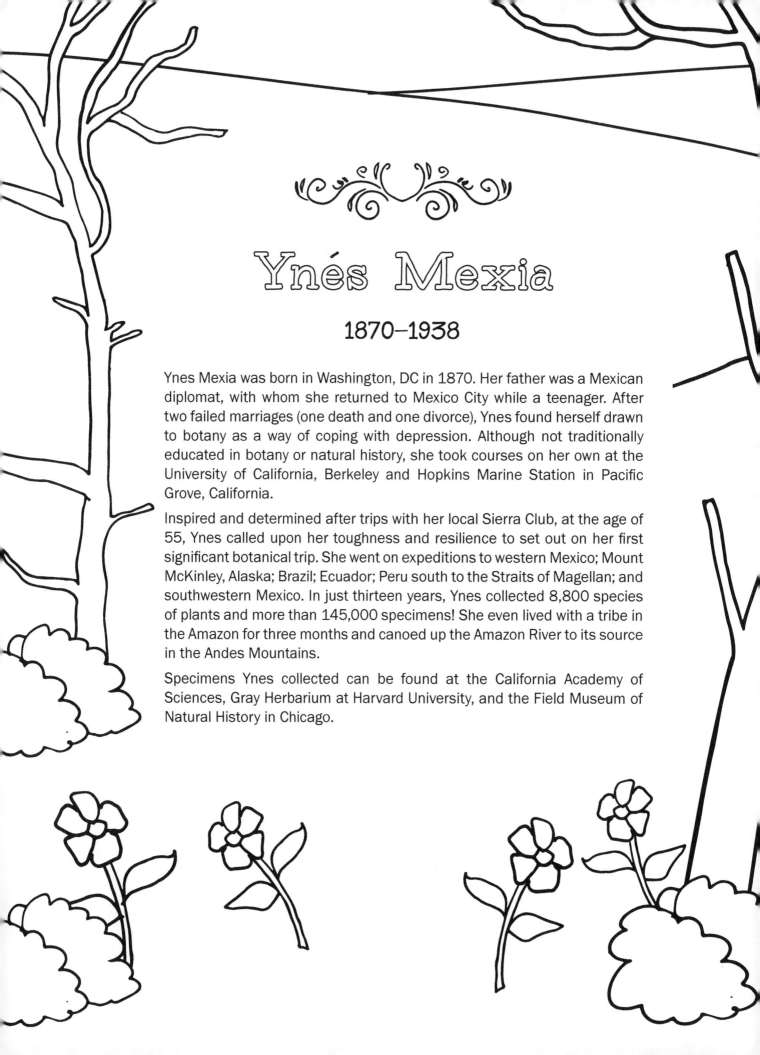

Ynés Mexia

1870–1938

Ynes Mexia was born in Washington, DC in 1870. Her father was a Mexican diplomat, with whom she returned to Mexico City while a teenager. After two failed marriages (one death and one divorce), Ynes found herself drawn to botany as a way of coping with depression. Although not traditionally educated in botany or natural history, she took courses on her own at the University of California, Berkeley and Hopkins Marine Station in Pacific Grove, California.

Inspired and determined after trips with her local Sierra Club, at the age of 55, Ynes called upon her toughness and resilience to set out on her first significant botanical trip. She went on expeditions to western Mexico; Mount McKinley, Alaska; Brazil; Ecuador; Peru south to the Straits of Magellan; and southwestern Mexico. In just thirteen years, Ynes collected 8,800 species of plants and more than 145,000 specimens! She even lived with a tribe in the Amazon for three months and canoed up the Amazon River to its source in the Andes Mountains.

Specimens Ynes collected can be found at the California Academy of Sciences, Gray Herbarium at Harvard University, and the Field Museum of Natural History in Chicago.

Ynés Mexia

Botanist

Glossary

Algae: plant-like organisms that live in water but do not have stems, roots, or leaves (while some algae are single-celled organisms, others, like seaweeds, are multicellular).

Algorithm: a set of rules to solve a problem or calculation, usually referring to computers.

Analytical Machine: also called an analytical engine, an 1837 design by English mathematician Charles Babbage for an early computer-like mechanical machine for general-purpose use; the successor to his difference engine.

Aquariophily: the keeping of fish and other marine organisms in aquariums for leisure or study.

Astronomy: the branch of science that looks at objects in space such as galaxies, stars, planets, asteroids, and comets; someone who studies astronomy is called an astronomer.

Biology: the branch of science that looks at living things; someone who studies biology is called a biologist.

Botany: a more focused branch of biology that looks at plants; someone who studies botany is called a botanist.

Chemistry: the branch of science that looks at the makeup, structure, and properties of matter (often focused on the Periodic Table of Elements); someone who studies chemistry is called a chemist.

Chromosome: in living cells, a threadlike structure that contains DNA (Deoxyribonucleic acid, the genetic material of an organism which determines the characteristics of its offspring).

Comet: an icy object in space that orbits the Sun and releases gasses when heated by sunlight on its inward approach, possibly showing a hazy tail when viewed from the Earth.

Congressional resolution: a legislative measure in the United States Congress that is voted on by the House of Representatives or the Senate, or in the case of resolutions that may become law, both houses (with either the President approving it or States ratifying it). One type of resolution, a simple resolution, can be used to recognize people or groups for an achievement.

Constellation: a group of stars in the night sky that appear to show a recognizable pattern, such as an animal or character from Greek mythology; today, astronomers recognize 88 constellations.

Difference Engine: also called difference machine, a design for a mechanical calculating machine by the English mathematician Charles Babbage, developed in the 1820s and 30s; later followed by his design for the analytical machine.

Ecology: the branch of science that looks at the factors that affect the relationship between living things and their environment, often through experimentation; someone who studies ecology is called an ecologist.

Electric arc: a visible electrical discharge between two electrodes or other points (lightning is an example of an electric arc).

Entomology: a more focused branch of biology that looks at insects and sometimes other bugs and invertebrates (no bones) such as arachnids, earthworms, and land snails and slugs; someone who studies entomology is called an entomologist.

Extinction: the dying out of a species of organism, either from the past and known through the fossil record, or currently through largely human effects on species' habitats.

Fossil: the preserved remains or traces of animals, plants, and other organisms, either as bones (as in dinosaur skeletons) or as trace fossils (preserved footprints, skin or leaf impressions, fossilized poop, etc.).

Fungi: a group of organisms, some appearing plant-like, that reproduce with spores, including yeast, molds, and mushrooms.

General theory of relativity: Albert Einstein's 1916 theory in **physics** that describes the force of gravity; it states that large objects in space, such as stars, can bend or curve space and time (this explains why planets orbit the Sun; the Sun is so massive that it bends the "fabric" of space, warping the straight line that planets would move in into curved orbits).

Geodesy: the study of the earth's physical features through the use of measurement and mathematics.

Geology: the branch of science that looks at the solid and liquid structure of the Earth, how rocks are formed, and the processes of landform change; someone who studies geology is called a geologist.

Histology: a more focused branch of biology that looks at the structure of cells and tissues in plants and animals.

Home economics: or domestic science or home ecology, the study of the economics and management of the home and community; finding ways to live and organize the home in harmony with the environment.

Hydrodynamics: the branch of science that looks at the forces acting on or exerted by fluids (such as liquids).

Laws of mechanical physics: also called classical mechanics or Newtonian mechanics, the set of physical laws describing the motion of bodies under the influence of a system of forces.

Lichen: an organism that consists of algae and fungi in a symbiotic relationship; those that appear bushy or leafy are called macrolichens, and can often be seen growing on trees.

Lunar eclipse: a celestial event in which the Moon passes directly behind the Earth into its shadow; direct light from the Sun is blocked, resulting in the Moon appearing reddish.

Marine: having to do with the oceanic parts of the Earth; not the land or air.

Mathematics: the study of numbers and patterns of numbers; many branches of science depend on mathematics for measurement, calculations, and formulas; someone who studies mathematics is called a mathematician.

Metamorphosis: the process of transformation in insects from one stage of development to another, such as a caterpillar metamorphosing into a butterfly.

Metaphysics: a branch of philosophy that looks at the ideas of being, knowing, and causation, among others.

Mollusk: a soft-bodied invertebrate animal (no bones), either **marine** or **terrestrial**, and some with a hard shell; examples include cephalopods (octopus, squid, and relatives), gastropods (slugs and snails), and bivalves (clams and mussels).

Natural History: the branch of science that looks at living things and their relationship to their environment through observation; someone who studies natural history is called a naturalist.

Nebula: a cloud of dust and gas in space, often where new stars will be formed.

Nuclear fission: the splitting of the nucleus of an atom, which causes a chain reaction of splitting, resulting in the release of a large amount of energy.

Nuclear physics: a more focused branch of physics that looks at the structure and interactions within atomic nuclei (whereas atomic physics looks at both nuclei and the electrons within atoms).

Ornithology: a more focused branch of biology that looks at birds; someone who studies ornithology is called an ornithologist.

Paleontology: the study of past life (animals, plants, and other organisms) using fossil remains that are dug out from rock layers; someone who studies paleontology is called a paleontologist.

Photometry: the study of the measurement of light as it is perceived by the human eye.

Physics: the branch of science that looks at matter and its motion and behavior through space and time; someone who studies physics is called a physicist.

Radiation: the emission or transmission of energy in the form of waves or particles through space or matter; some forms of radiation can damage living tissue.

Radioactivity: a type of radiation in which the nuclei of certain atoms (the central part of an atom consisting of protons and neutrons), such as radium and uranium, emit high energy particles and rays.

Sanitation: the effort to improve public health by providing clean drinking water and adequate sewage disposal.

Seismology: a more focused branch of geology that looks at the causes and effects of earthquakes and other movements of the Earth's crust.

Solar eclipse: a celestial event in which the Moon passes between the Earth and the Sun, partially or fully blocking light from the Sun and darkening the sky for a short period of time.

Solar Ray: radiation from the Sun; we know it in our everyday experience on Earth as sunlight.

Taxonomy: the branch of science that looks at how to classify living things.

Terrestrial: having to do with the land parts of the Earth, not the oceans or air.

Theoretical physics: a more focused branch of physics that uses mathematical models to explain and predict natural phenomena (whereas experimental physics uses prediction, observation, and analysis to understand natural phenomena).

Vertebrate: an animal with a backbone; animals without backbones are called invertebrates.

X-ray: an invisible electromagnetic ray that can pass through some materials; doctors and dentists use X-rays to see bones, organs, and inside teeth.

Zoology: a more focused branch of biology that looks at animals, such as mammals (mammalogy), birds (ornithology), reptiles and amphibians (herpetology), fish (ichthyology), or insects (entomology); someone who studies zoology is called a zoologist.

Resources

General

A Mighty Girl
Amightygirl.com

Amy Poehler's Smart Girls
Amysmartgirls.com

FearlesslyGirl
Fearlesslygirl.com

Girls are Powerful
Girlsarepowerful.com

Girls for a Change
Girlsforachange.org

Girls Inc.
Girlsinc.com

Girl Rising
Girlrising.com

Girl Up (United Nations Foundation)
Girlup.org

He for She
Heforshe.org

Kazoo Magazine
Kazoomagazine.com

Science + Technology + Engineering + Mathematics

American Association of University Women
Aauw.org

Association for Women Geoscientists
http://www.awg.org/

Association for Women in Mathematics
https://sites.google.com/site/awmmath/home

Association for Women in Science
AWIS.org

Black Girls Code
Blackgirlscode.com

Committee on the Status of Women in Astronomy
Cswa.aas.org

Girlstart
Girlstart.org

Girls Who Code
Girlswhocode.com

Jane Goodall's Roots and Shoots
Rootsandshoots.org

Lady Science
Ladyscience.com

Latinas in STEM
Latinasinstem.com

Million Women Mentors
Millionwomenmentors.org

Mission Blue
Mission-blue.org

myFossil
Myfossil.org

National Girls Collaborative Project
NGCProject.org

National Math and Science Initiative
NMS.org

oStem
Ostem.com

Scientista
Scientisafoundation.com

Science Cheerleader
Sciencecheerleader.com

Smore Magazine
Smoremagazine.com

STEM Women
Stemwomen.net

Trowelblazers
Trowelblazers.com

Women in Astronomy
Womeninastronomy.blogspot.com

Women in Bio
Womeninbio.org

Women in Engineering ProActive Network
Wepan.org

Women in Physics (APS)
www.aps.org/programs/women/index.cfm

Women in Planetary Science
womeninplanetaryscience.wordpress.com

500 Women Scientists
500womenscientists.org

Online Exhibits

Biodiversity Heritage Library: Early Women in Science

Women Who Figure: An Exhibit Inspired by the Mathematicians of Hidden Figures: Great Women of Mathematics

4000 Years of Women in Science

Museums/Associations/Organizations/Events/Awards/Books, etc.
An asterisk (*) denotes books that are specifically for younger readers

Ada Lovelace

Ada Lovelace Day, "an international celebration day of the achievements of women in science, technology, engineering and maths (STEM)" occurs every year on the second Tuesday of October

Ada Lovelace Award from the Association for Women in Computing

Books

*Fiona Robinson, *Ada's Ideas: The Story of Ada Lovelace, the World's First Computer Programmer* (New York: Abrams Books for Young Readers, 2016)

*Laurie Wallmark, *Ada Byron Lovelace and the Thinking Machine* (Berkeley, CA: Creston Books, 2015)

James Essinger, *Ada's Algorithm: How Lord Byron's Daughter Ada Lovelace Launched the Digital Age* (Brooklyn, NY: Melville House, 2015)

Dorothy Stein, *Ada: A Life And A Legacy* (Cambridge, MA: MIT Press, 1987)

Alice Ball

Alice Augusta Ball Endowed Scholarship Fund at the University of Hawai'i

Books

Sam Maggs, *Wonder Women: 25 Innovators, Inventors, and Trailblazers Who Changed History* (Philadelphia: Quirk Books, 2016)

Amalie Emmy Noether

Emmy Noether Lectures from Association for Women in Mathematics, "to honor women who have made fundamental and sustained contributions to the mathematical sciences"

Emmy Noether Award from Brown Foundation, for young female scientists (in high school) in Louisiana and Mississippi

Emmy Noether Distinction for Women in Physics from from European Physical Society, "to enhance the recognition of noteworthy women physicists with a strong connection to Europe through nationality or work"

Emmy Noether Visiting Fellowships from Perimeter Institute for Theoretical Physics, for "outstanding theoretical physicists who wish to pursue research at the institute while on leave from their faculty positions at home institutes"

Emmy Noether Society at the University of Cambridge, "to promote women studying mathematical sciences"

Books

*M.B.W. Tent, *Emmy Noether: The Mother of Modern Algebra* (Boca Raton, FL: Taylor & Francis, 2008)

Dwight E. Neuenschwander, *Emmy Noether's Wonderful Theorem* (Baltimore: Johns Hopkins University Press, 2017 [revised and updated from 2010]) – a technical work

James W. Brewer and Martha K. Smith, *Emmy Noether: A Tribute to Her Life and Work* (New York: Marcel Dekker, 1981)

Anna Atkins

Books

Carol Armstrong and Catherine de Zegher, eds., *Ocean Flowers: Impressions from Nature* (Princeton University Press, 2004)

Anna Botsford Comstock

Books

*Suzanne Slade, *Out of School and Into Nature: The Anna Comstock Story* (Ann Arbor, MI: Sleeping Bear Press, 2017)

Sally Gregory Kohlstedt, *Teaching Children Science: Hands-On Nature Study in North America, 1890-1930* (Chicago: University of Chicago Press, 2010)

Annie Jump Cannon

Annie Jump Cannon Award in Astronomy from the American Astronomical Society, for "outstanding research and promise for future research by a postdoctoral woman researcher"

Books

*Carole Gerber, *Annie Jump Cannon, Astronomer* (Gretna, LA: Pelican Publishing, 2011)

Dava Sobel, *The Glass Universe: How the Ladies of the Harvard Observatory Took the Measure of the Stars* (New York: Viking, 2016)

Beatrix Potter

National Trust Beatrix Potter Awards, for recognizing local people for conservation, land use, farming, story illustration, and service to community

Hill Top, Potter's first house in the Lake District

Beatrix Potter Society

Books

A Celebration of Beatrix Potter: Art and letters by more than 30 of today's favorite children's book illustrators (New York: Frederick Warne/Penguin Books, 2016)

Linda Lear, *Beatrix Potter: A Life in Nature* (New York: St. Martin's Press, 2016)

Caroline Herschel

Herschel Museum of Astronomy in Bath, England (historic home)

Books

*Emily Arnold McCully, *Caroline's Comets: A True Story Hardcover* (New York: Holiday House, 2017)

Michael Hoskin, *Caroline Herschel: Priestess of the New Heavens* (Sagamore Beach, MA: Science History Publications, 2013)

Marilyn B. Ogilvie, *Searching the Stars: The Story of Caroline Herschel* (Gloucestershire, England: History Press, 2008)

Dr. Emily Winterburn, *The Quiet Revolution of Caroline Herschel: The Lost Heroine of Astronomy* (Stroud, UK: The History Press, 2017)

Dorothea Bate

Books

Karolyn Shindler, *Discovering Dorothea: The Life of the Pioneering Fossil-Hunter Dorothea Bate* (HarperCollins, 2005)

Ellen Swallow Richards

Ellen Swallow Richards Public Service Award from the Board on Human Sciences, "to honor a nationally recognized leader who has a significant history of promoting and advancing the Human Sciences"

Ellen Swallow Richards Diversity Award from The Minerals, Metals & Materials Society, "recognizes an individual who, in the remarkable pioneering spirit of Ellen Swallow Richards, has helped or inspired others to overcome personal, professional, educational, cultural, or institutional adversity to pursue a career in minerals, metals, and/or materials"

Books
*Ethlie Ann Vare, *Adventurous Spirit: A Story About Ellen Swallow Richards* (Carolrhoda Books, 1992)
Samuel A. Goldblith, *Of Microbes and Molecules: Food Technology, Nutrition and Applied Biology at M.I.T., 1873-1988* (Trumbell, CT: Food & Nutrition Press, c1995)
Thomas Kwai Lam, *Science and Culture: Ellen Swallow Richards and Nineteenth Century Nutritional Science* (Baltimore: Johns Hopkins University, 1981)
Pamela C. Swallow, *The Remarkable Life and Career of Ellen Swallow Richards: Pioneer in Science and Technology* (Wiley-TMS, 2014)

Émilie du Châtelet

The Émilie Du Châtelet Award from the Women's Caucus of ASECS is an annual prize of $500, "to support research in progress by an independent or adjunct scholar on a feminist or Women's Studies subject"

Books
Robyn Arianrhod, *Seduced by Logic: Émilie Du Châtelet, Mary Somerville and the Newtonian Revolution* (New York: Oxford University Press, 2012)
Judith P. Zinsser, *Émilie Du Châtelet: Daring Genius of the Enlightenment* (New York: Penguin, 2007)

Genevieve Jones

Books
Joy M. Kiser, *America's Other Audubon* (New York: Princeton Architectural Press, 2012)

Henrietta Swan Leavitt

Books
*Robert Burleigh, *Look Up!: Henrietta Leavitt, Pioneering Woman Astronomer* (New York: Simon & Schuster, 2013)
George Johnson, *Miss Leavitt's Stars: The Untold Story of the Woman Who Discovered How to Measure the Universe* (New York: W. W. Norton, 2006)
Dava Sobel, *The Glass Universe: How the Ladies of the Harvard Observatory Took the Measure of the Stars* (New York: Viking, 2016)

Hertha Marks Ayrton

Hertha Ayrton Research Fellowship at Girton College, Cambridge

Inge Lehman

Inge Lehmann Medal from the American Geophysical Union, for "outstanding contributions to the understanding of the structure, composition, and dynamics of the Earth's mantle and core"

Jeanne Baré

Books
Glynis Ridley, *The Discovery of Jeanne Baret: A Story of Science, the High Seas, and the First Woman to Circumnavigate the Globe* (New York: Broadway Books, 2010)

Lise Meitner

Lise Meitner Prize in "Nuclear Science" from European Physical Society
Lise Meitner Award Fellowship from the Max Planck Institute for Informatics
Lise Meitner Society, "aim is the equality of women in science and mathematics within and outside the academic career"

Books
*Winifred Conkling, *Radioactive!: How Irène Curie and Lise Meitner Revolutionized Science and Changed the World* (Chapel Hill, NC: Algonquin Young Readers, 2016)
Ruth Lewin Sime, *Lise Meitner: A Life in Physics* (Berkeley: University of California Press, 1997)

Maria Sibylla Merian

Maria Sibylla Merian-Prize from the Essen College of Gender Studiesat Universität Duisburg-Essen, "given to women scientists for their outstanding achievements mainly in the natural and technical sciences, as well as in medicine"
Academy Merian Prize from Royal Netherlands Academy of Arts and Sciences, "awarded to outstanding female researchers working for Dutch research organisations who had inspired others to embark on careers in science or scholarship"
Maria Sibylla Merian Society

Books
*Margarita Engle and Julie Paschkis (illustrator), *Summer Birds: The Butterflies of Maria Merian* (New York: Henry Holt and Co., 2010)
*Jeannine Atkins, *Finding Wonders: Three Girls Who Changed Science* (New York: Atheneum Books for Young Readers, 2016)
Kim Todd, Chrysalis: *Maria Sibylla Merian and the Secrets of Metamorphosis* (New York: Harcourt Books, 2007)
Ella Reitsma, *Maria Sibylla Merian and Daughters: Women of Art and Science* (New York: Oxford University Press, 2008)

Maria Mitchell

Maria Mitchell Association

Books
*Jeannine Atkins, *Finding Wonders: Three Girls Who Changed Science* (New York: Atheneum Books for Young Readers, 2016)
*Deborah Hopkinson, *Maria's Comet* (New York: Atheneum/Anne Schwartz Books, 1999)
*Beatrice Gormley, *Maria Mitchell: The Soul of an Astronomer* (Grand Rapids, MI: Eerdmans Books for Young Readers, 2003)
Renee Bergland, *Maria Mitchell and the Sexing of Science: An Astronomer Among the American Romantics* (Boston, MA: Beacon Press, 2008)

Marie Curie and Irène Curie

Musee Curie Museum In Paris
Maria Skłodowska-Curie Museum in Warsaw, Poland

The Marie Curie Award from the Radiation Research Society, "to recognize the Scholars-in-Training travel award applicant showing the highest potential for a successful career in radiation research"

Marie Curie Fellows Association

Marie Sklodowska-Curie Award from the IEEE, "For outstanding contributions to the field of nuclear and plasma sciences and engineering"

Books

*Kathleen Krull, *Giants of Science: Marie Curie* (New York: Viking Juvenile, 2007)

*Amy M. O'Quinn, *Marie Curie for Kids: Her Life and Scientific Discoveries, with 21 Activities and Experiments* (Chicago: Chicago Review Press, 2016)

Marilyn Ogilvie, *Marie Curie: A Biography* (Westport, CT: Greenwood Press, 2004)

Barbara Goldsmith, *Obsessive Genius: The Inner World of Marie Curie* (New York: W.W. Norton, 2005)

Mary Anning

Lyme Regis Museum

Mary Anning Award from the The Palaeontological Association (UK), "open to all those who are not professionally employed within palaeontology but who have made an outstanding contribution to the subject"

Books

*Laurence Anholt, *Stone Girl Bone Girl: The Story of Mary Anning of Lyme Regis* (London: Frances Lincoln, 2006)

*Monica Kulling, *Mary Anning's Curiosity* (Toronto: Groundwood Books, 2017)

*Catherine Brighton, *The Fossil Girl* (London: Frances Lincoln, 2007)

Shelley Emling, *The Fossil Hunter: Dinosaurs, Evolution, and the Woman Whose Discoveries Changed the World* (New York: St. Martin's Press, 2011)

Christopher McGowan, *The Dragon Seekers: How an Extraordinary Circle of Fossilists Discovered the Dinosaurs and Paved the Way for Darwin* (Cambridge, MA: Perseus Publishing, 2001)

Mary Somerville

Mary Somerville Medal and Prize from Institute of Physics, "for exceptional early career contributions to public engagement within physics"

Books

Robyn Arianrhod, *Seduced by Logic: Émilie Du Châtelet, Mary Somerville and the Newtonian Revolution* (New York: Oxford University Press, 2012)

Kathryn A. Neeley, *Mary Somerville: Science, Illumination, and the Female Mind* (New York: Cambridge University Press, 2001)

Mary Treat

Books

Tina Gianquitto, *'Good observers of nature': American women and the scientific study of the natural world, 1820–1885* (Athens, GA: University of Georgia Press, 2007), one chapter covers Treat

Roger Arliner Young

Books

Wini Warren, "Roger Arliner Young: A Cautionary Tale," in *Black Women Scientists in the United States* (Bloomington, IN: Indiana University Press, 1999)

Forthcoming, an academic book by Sara P. Díaz about Roger Arliner Young, tentatively titled *Doing Science from the Back of the Bus*

Sofia Kovalevskaya

Memorial Museum-Estate of Sofia Kovalevskaya in Polibino, Russia

Sofja Kovalevskaja Award from the Alexander von Humboldt Foundation, "given to promising young academics to pursue their line of research in the sciences or arts and humanities" in Germany

Books

Michele Audin, *Remembering Sofya Kovalevskaya* (London: Springer, 2011)

Ann Koblitz, *A Convergence of Lives: Sofia Kovalevskaia: Scientist, Writer, Revolutionary* (New Brunswick, NJ: Rutgers University Press, 1993)

Ynés Mexia

Books

*Durlynn Anema, *Ynés Mexia: Botanist and Adventurer* (Greensboro, NC: Morgan Reynolds Publishing, 2005)

More Pioneering Women in Science

Maria Margarethe Kirch (1670-1720)
Astronomer and Mathematician

Jane Colden (1724-1766)
Botanist

Charlotte Murchison (1788-1869)
Geologist

Mary Buckland (1797-1857)
Marine Biologist, Paleontologist, and
Scientific Illustrator

Mary Lyell (1808-1873)
Conchologist and Geologist

Elizabeth Cabot Agassiz (1822-1907)
Naturalist and Scientific Writer

Marianne North (1830-1890)
Botanical Illustrator and Biologist

Agnes Mary Clerke (1842-1907)
Astronomer

Katherine Brandagee (1844-1920)
Botanist

Marg Blagg (1858-1944)
Astronomer

Alice Eastwood (1859-1953)
Botanist

Annie Montague Alexander (1867-1950)
Paleontologist

Mary Agnes Chase (1869-1963)
Botanical Illustrator and Botanist

Marion Newbigin (1869-1934)
Biologist

Edith Patch (1876-1954)
Entomologist

Agnes Robertson Arber (1879-1960)
Plant Morphologist and Anatomist

Maria Carmichael Stopes (1880-1958)
Botanist

Lucy Evelyn Cheesman (1882-1969)
Entomologist

Ann Haven Morgan (1882-1966)
Zoologist and Ecologist

Libby Hyman (1888-1969)
Zoologist

Emma Lucy Braun (1889-1971)
Botanist and Ecologist

Marietta Blau (1894-1970)
Physicist

Sheila Macalister Marshall (1896-1977)
Marine Biologist

Doris Mable Cochran (1898-1968)
Herpetologist

Elizabeth Lorayne is an award-winning author and publisher of children's books. After the success of her series *The Adventures of Piratess Tilly*, whose heroine is a budding naturalist and the captain of her own ship, Elizabeth continues to produce books with themes of girl-empowerment, eco-consciousness, exploration, and science. She is an artist and mother, inspired by nature, history, and the rhythms of her surroundings. Elizabeth is a graduate of The New School in New York City and a current member of the Society of Children's Book Writers and Illustrators. She resides in Newburyport, Massachusetts with her family.

To find out more about Elizabeth and the Piratess Tilly series, please visit PiratessTilly.com and Elizabethlorayne.com.

Kendra Shedenhelm is an artist, mom, cat-lover and many other things. Born and raised in Nebraska, she graduated with her BFA in Chicago in 1995, and has since worked as a painter, printmaker, illustrator, and designer throughout the Midwest, Colorado, Los Angeles, and New York City.

Visit the illustrator's website at Kendrashedenhelm.com

Special Thanks
to these
Kickstarter Backers

Lori Tierney

The Jackman Family of Newburyport

Mrs. C. F. Miller

Mel the Engineer, host of the STEMxm podcast

CPSIA information can be obtained
at www.ICGtesting.com
Printed in the USA
LVHW082206040619
620177LV00037B/976/P